THE

INTERNATIONAL LIBRARY

OF

PIANO MUSIC

ALBUM TWELVE

THE
INTERNATIONAL LIBRARY
OF
PIANO MUSIC

1968

THE UNIVERSITY SOCIETY, Inc.
Educational Publishers since 1897
New York

In addition to its wealth of contemporary material, this *new* INTERNATIONAL LIBRARY OF PIANO MUSIC combines the most successful teaching and playing masterpieces of its predecessors; namely:

TECHNIQUE

(STUDIES AND EXERCISES)

compiled and edited

by

DENES AGAY

TABLE OF CONTENTS
in order of studies

ALBUM TWELVE

The 12 Major Scales and the 12 Minor Scales

4

5

Db major

Bb minor (harmonic)

Bb minor (melodic)

B major

G# minor (harmonic)

G# minor (melodic)

E major

C# minor (harmonic)

C# minor (melodic)

10

A major

F# minor (harmonic)

F# minor (melodic)

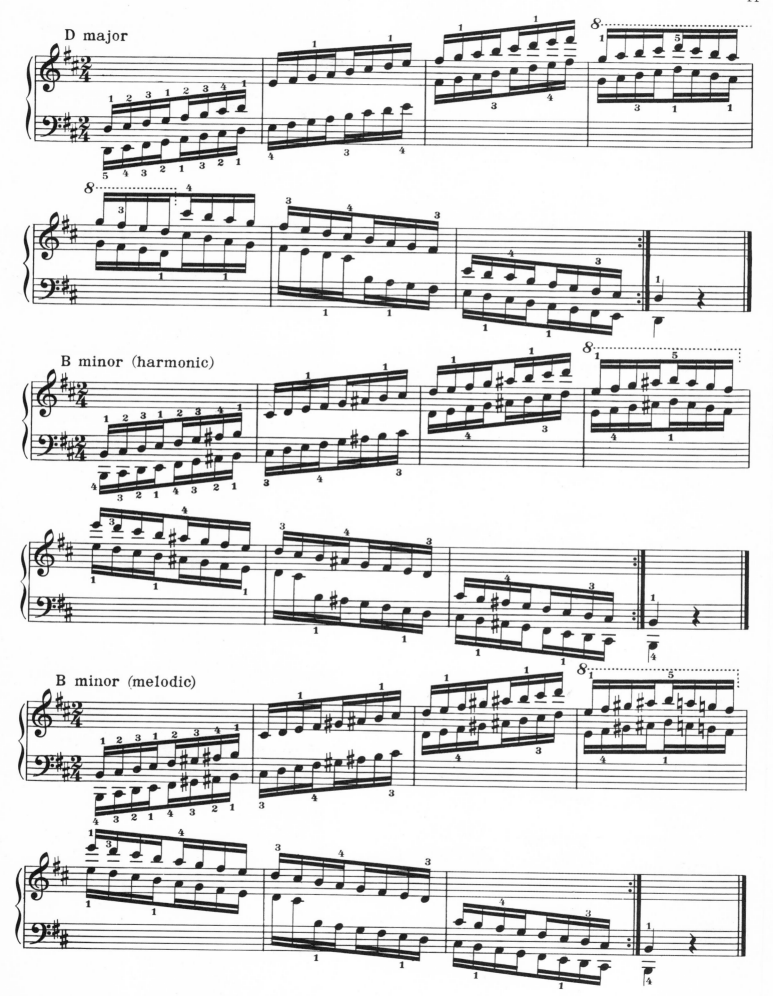

D major

B minor (harmonic)

B minor (melodic)

Rapid scales, arpeggios

Carl Czerny

2

Rapid, legato scale passages

Albert Loeschhorn

3 Allegro

Rapid finger staccato

Vadim Salmanov

4 Molto vivo

Left hand study; finger staccato

Carl Czerny

5

6 Allegro risoluto

Hermann Berens

20

Chord study; wrist staccato

Henri Lemoine

7 Allegretto

Fine

f

p

mf

p   cresc.

rit.

D. C. al Fine

Two-voice scale study; clear tone, precise rhythm, firm finger action

8

Allegretto

Sigismund Lebert and Louis Stark

Study in phrasing, expression and use of damper pedal

Stephen Heller

9

Andante con moto

LE RETOUR

Repeated double notes and chords in fast tempo; wrist staccato

Friedrich Burgmüller

10

Molto agitato quasi presto

11

28

30

F# major

F# minor

F# major

F# minor

C# major (Enharmonic Equivalent: Db)

C# minor

Broken chord passages; slight rotation of wrist and forearm

Henri Bertini

RAPID BROKEN CHORD PATTERNS IN UNISON

Play with a "light" fore-arm, suspended at the shoulders

Carl Czerny

13 Allegro

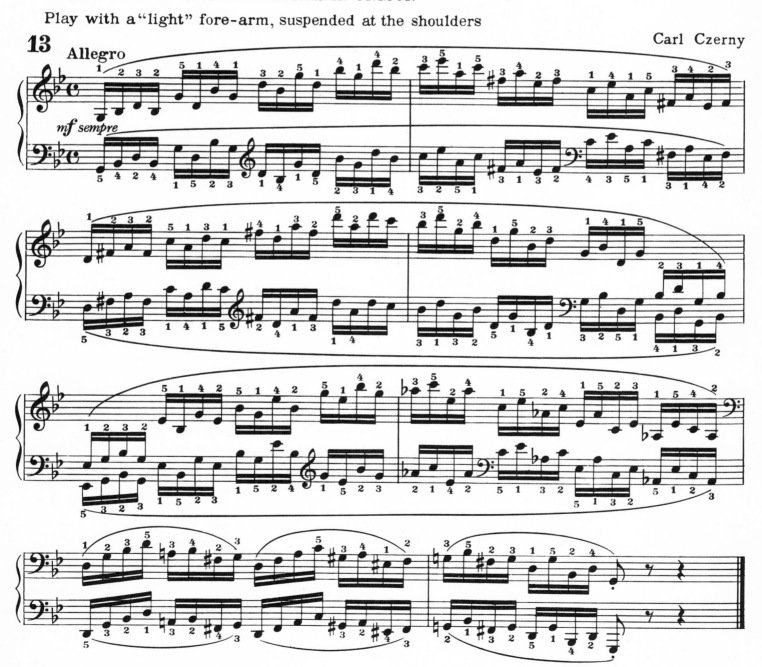

Slight pressure touch on the long notes in both hands; damper pedal study

14 Moderato

Carl Czerny

Ped. simile

PRAEAMBULUM
Two-voice invention

Johann Sebastian Bach

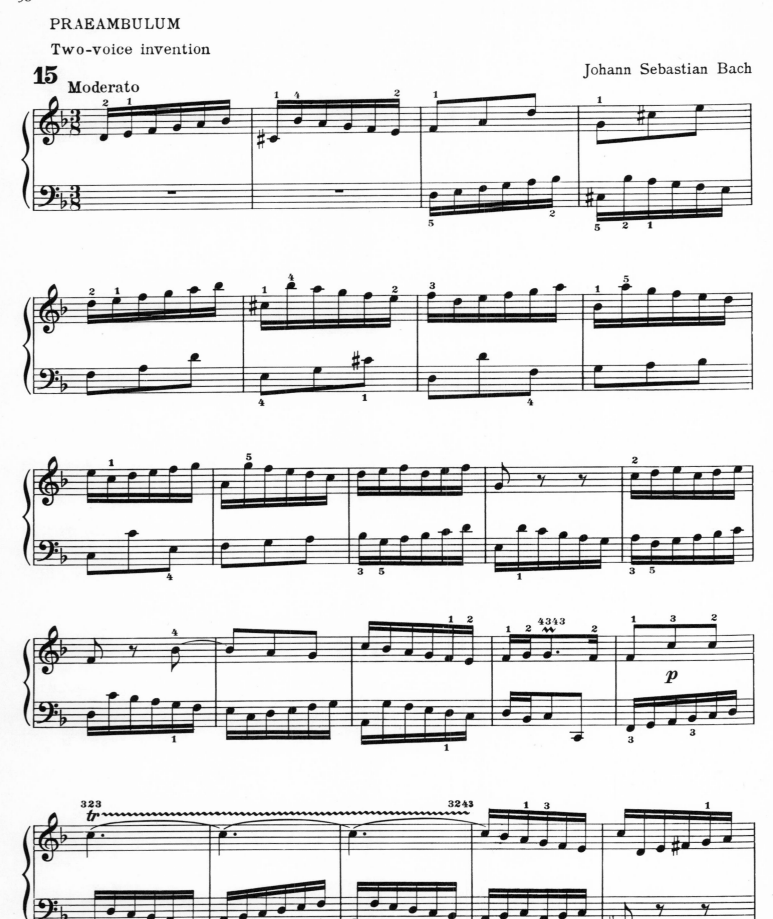

Scale study in rhythmic, polyphonic playing

Henri Bertini

16 Allegro

Polyphonic playing; practice hands separately at first

17 **Allegro**   Henri Bertini

ben sostenuto il canto

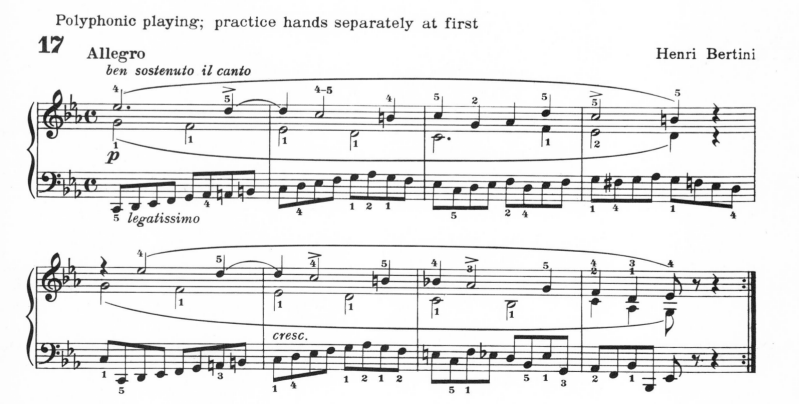

Extended Arpeggios in all Major and Minor Keys

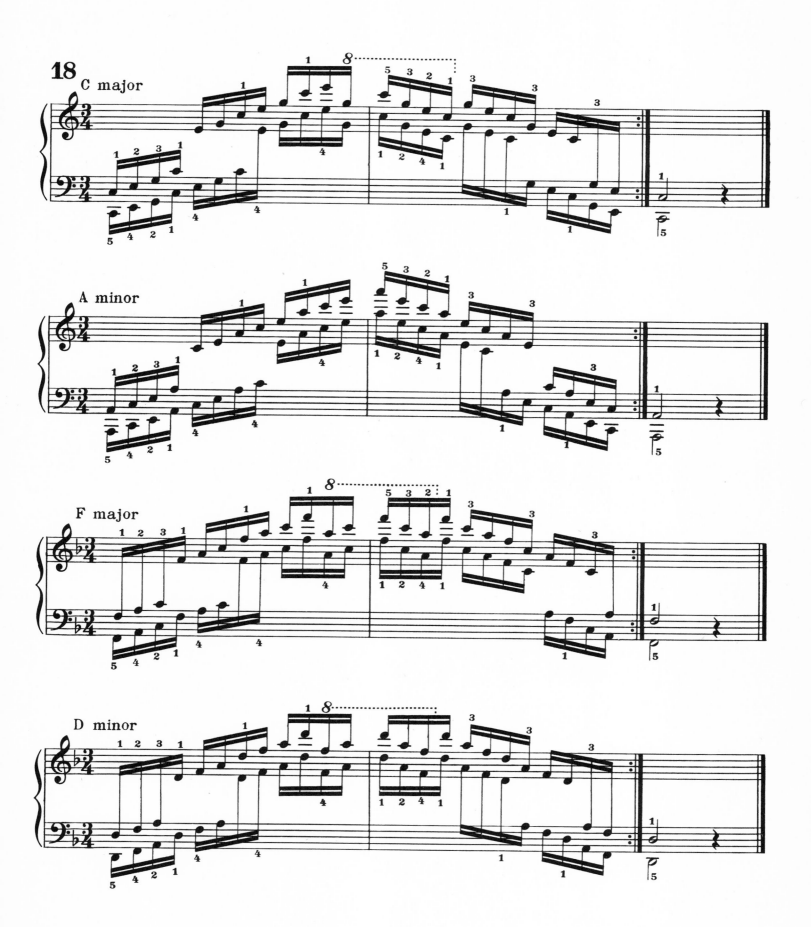

44

46

48

Quick passage of thumb

Carl Czerny

19 Allegretto

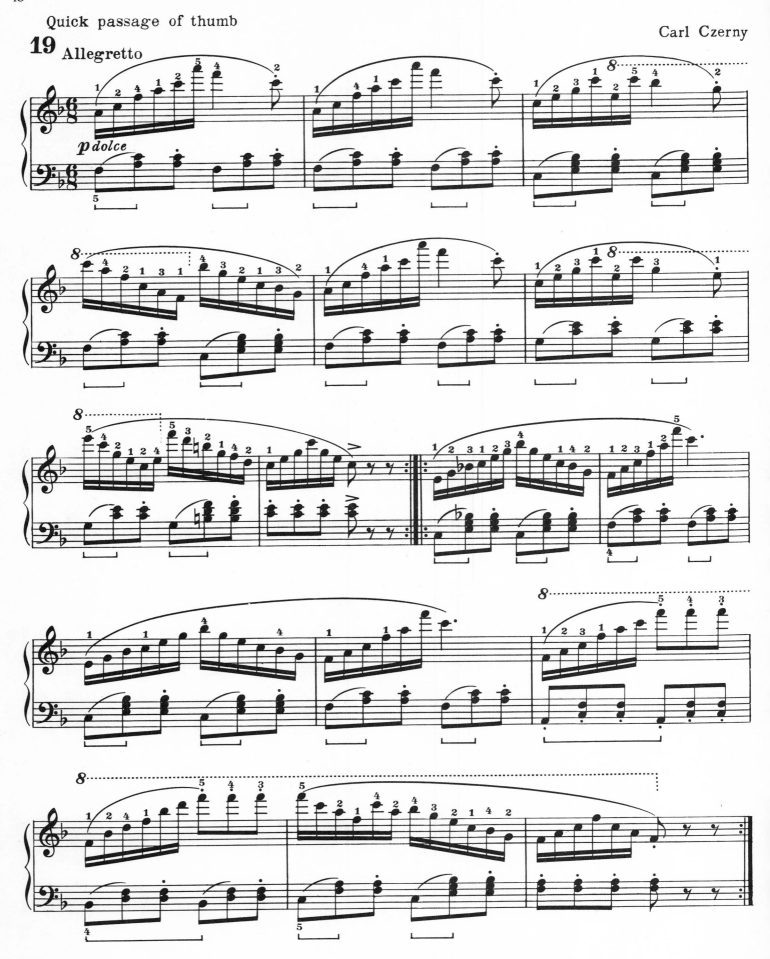

Flexibility and ease in continuous arpeggios

20 Allegro moderato

Jean B. Duvernoy

TWO ARPEGGIO ETUDES

Carl Czerny

Firm finger action; rhythmic precision

23 Allegro

Dmitri Kabalevsky

senza Ped.

52

PRAEAMBULUM

Two-voice invention

Johann Sebastian Bach

24 Con moto

55

Chromatic Scales

25

At an octave

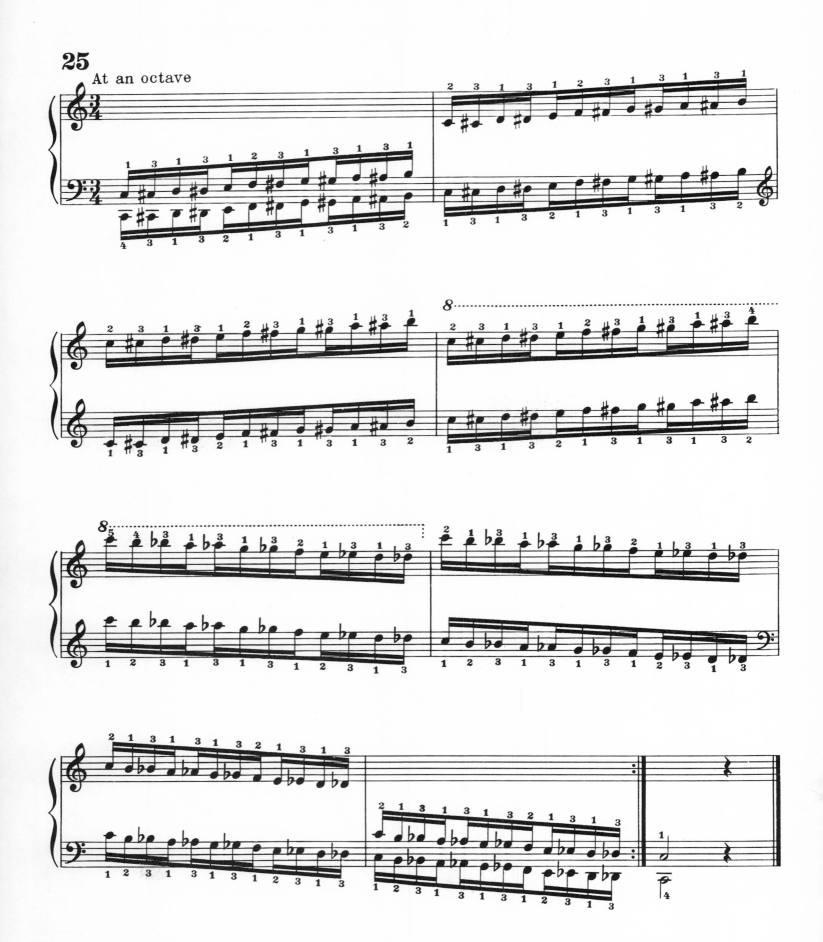

26

At a minor third

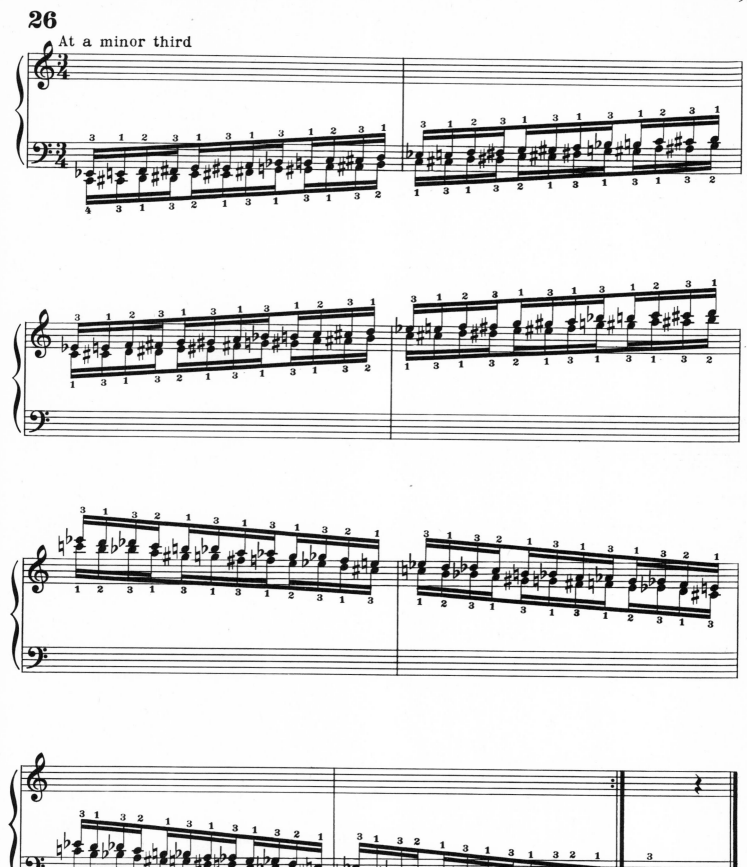

27

At a major sixth

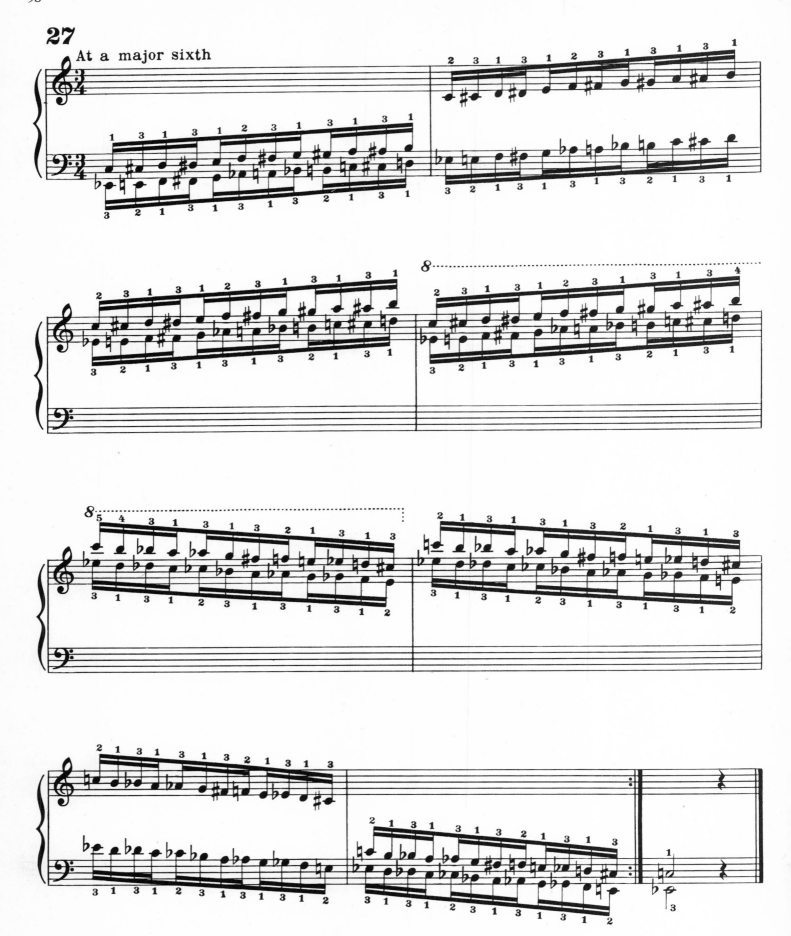

28

At a minor sixth

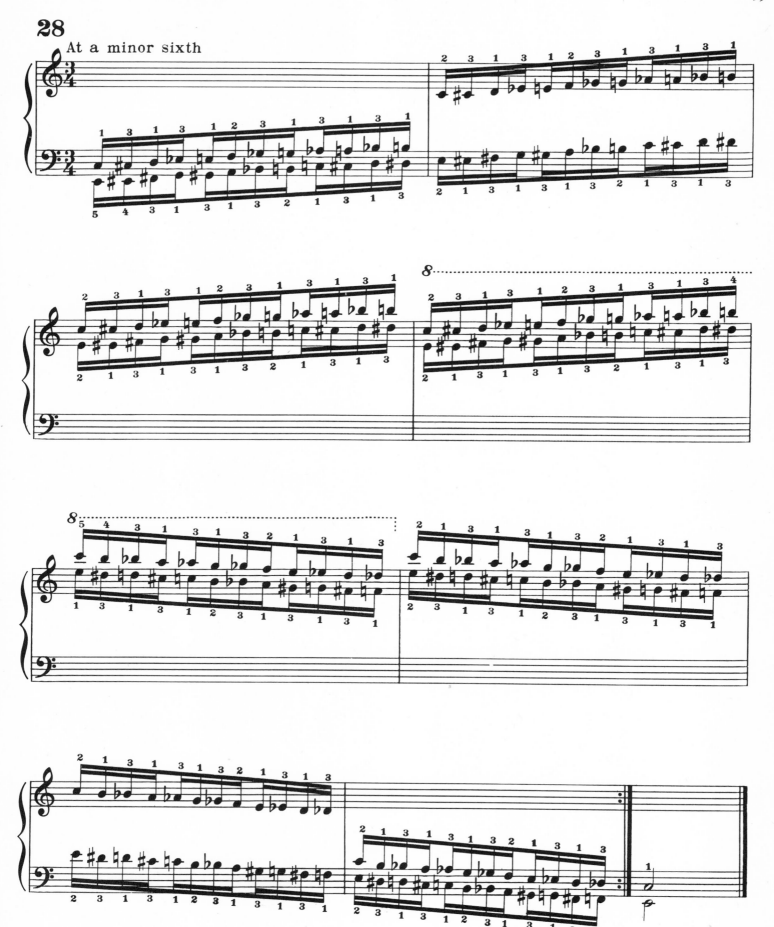

Light, fast chromatics

Friedrich Brauer

29 Allegro
leggiero

Chromatic scale passages in unison

Carl Czerny

30

Allegro

TWO STUDIES IN FOUR-VOICE PLAYING

Slight pressure on melody notes

Carl Czerny

Legatissimo and espressivo; observe fingering

Henri Bertini

33

Andante

Legato thirds in *L.H.*

34 Allegro moderato

Carl Czerny

Legato thirds in *R.H.*

35 Allegretto

Carl Czerny

66

Even finger action throughout; practice slowly at first

Mortimer Wilson

36
Moderato

TWO TRILL STUDIES

37

Albert Biehl

Allegro non troppo

38

Allegro non troppo

Albert Biehl

Trills

39 Andantino espressivo

Carl Czerny

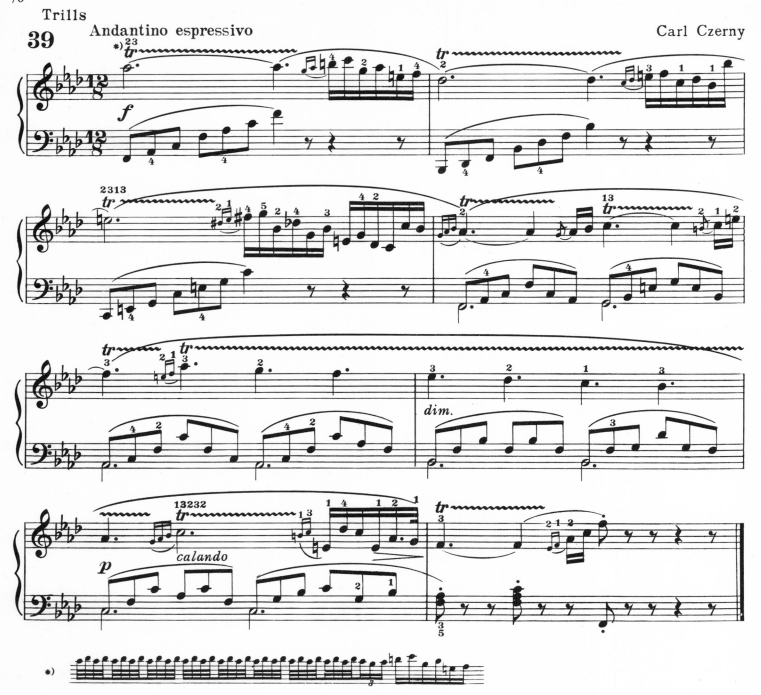

Even legato thirds

40 Moderato

Aloys Schmitt

GERMAN STUDENT SONG

Left hand melody in octaves

43

Gustav Damm

Wrist staccato

44

Allegretto

Henri Lemoine

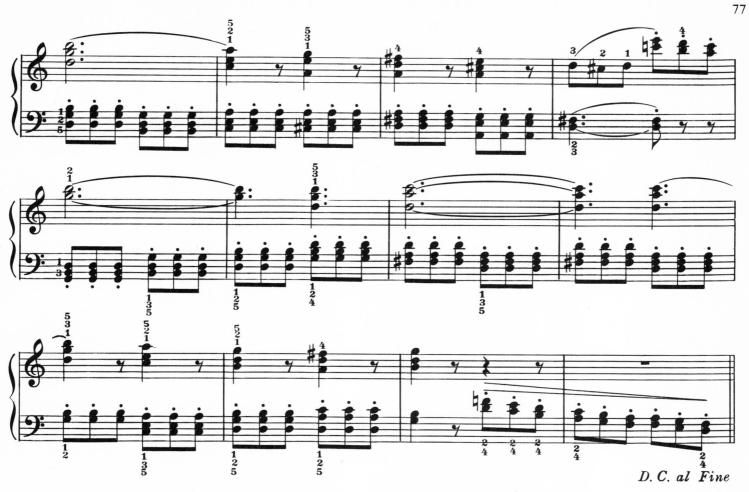

D. C. al Fine

Block chords hand over hand; practice slowly at first

Carl Czerny

45

78

Unison legato and staccato groups; interlocking chords, using fore-arm staccato

46

Alexander Goedicke

Left hand melody in staccato octaves; elastic wrist action

47

Allegro

Carl Czerny

Octave study using wrist staccato

48

Allegretto

Henri Bertini

Elastic wrist action

49

Allegretto giocoso

Carl Czerny

82

Velocity study for the right hand; even finger action, leggiero touch

50

Carl Czerny

Rapid groups with finger crossing; accented melodic tones

51

Allegro moderato

Félix Le Couppey

Velocity study for the left hand

55

Ignatz Pleyel

Allegro moderato

Play octaves with relaxed wrist action; avoid any muscle strain.

56

Carl Czerny

Allegretto

Study for velocity and independent finger action

57

Alexander Goedicke

Veloce

p legato sempre

Leggiero touch

58

Molto allegro

Carl Czerny

Leggiero touch

59

Molto allegro

Carl Czerny

p leggiermente

cresc.

dim.

60

Allegro risoluto

Hermann Berens

Chord and rhythm study, two against three

61

Allegro ma non troppo

Heinrich Germer

D.C. al Fine

Left hand study in broken chord velocity

Carl Czerny

62

Bring out melody clearly; perform with slight rotation

63

Allegro

Albert Loeschhorn

il canto marcato